SCHOOL'S OUT! LET'S SHOUT!

BY ROBIN WASSERMAN
ILLUSTRATED BY LAURA COYLE

SCHOLASTIC INC.

NEW YORK   TORONTO   LONDON   AUCKLAND   SYDNEY

MEXICO CITY   NEW DELHI   HONG KONG   BUENOS AIRES

FOR OFFICE FRIENDS
WHO MADE EVERY DAY
FEEL LIKE A VACATION.
(YOU KNOW WHO YOU ARE!)

ISBN 0-439-66487-X

12 11 10 9 8 7 6 5 4 3 2 1   4 5 6 7 8 9/0

PRINTED IN THE U.S.A.   40
FIRST PRINTING, MAY 2004

BOOK DESIGN BY JENNIFER RINALDI

WHat's InSiDe!

No More Pencils No More Books...

You waited and waited. You counted down the days, the minutes, even the seconds. You hoped and hoped that this day would finally come. Then you waited even more, until you couldn't wait any longer. And now, FINALLY, you're on

Vacation!

Congratulations—you made it! No more classes, no more homework, no more teachers—just recess and lunch, all day, every day. Your time is finally yours and you want to make the most of it. So what now?

Bored? Already? Have no fear, your 100% guaranteed school break boredom cure is here! This book has everything you need to have an amazing, awesome vacation. So get ready for a vacation you'll NEVER forget!

FRIENDS FOREVER

Time for summertime fun—but wait! First you have to personalize this book. Fill in this info about you and your friends, so that you'll always remember the people who shared the best summer of your life!

My name: _____

My age: _____

My school: _____

Day my vacation started: _____

Day my vacation will end (OH, NO!): _____

The best vacation I've ever had (so far) was when I

_____

_____

My BFFs: _____

_____

This vacation, my friends and I will definitely:

     1. _____

     2. _____

     3. _____

And we will definitely *not*:

     1. _____

     2. _____

     3. _____

Now fill in this space with a picture of you and your friends, pre-vacation—you can paste down a photo or draw one yourself!

TOP TEN

Okay, you may not like to admit it, but school can be fun sometimes...right? Even so, you would hate to have to go to school all year round. That's what vacation's for. So, what aren't you going to miss? (Check out the ideas below to get yourself started.)

TOP TEN THINGS I WON'T MISS ABOUT SCHOOL

10. _____

9. _____

8. "MYSTERY MEAT" DAY IN THE CAFETERIA

7. _____

6. RECESS...IN THE RAIN

5. _____

4. GETTING UP EARLY

3. _____

2. _____

And the #1 thing I *WON'T* miss about school is...

1. _____

SUMMER SCHOOL

What if you *did* have classes during your vacation? Check out some of the possibilities. There are still empty schedule slots, so go crazy and make up some cool classes!

9 a.m. 1st PERIOD	Strategies for Sleeping Late
10 a.m. 2nd PERIOD	Advanced Pool Games
11 a.m. 3rd PERIOD	Recess for Beginners
12 p.m. 4th PERIOD	Pizza Party
1 p.m. 5th PERIOD	Introduction to Ice Cream
2 p.m. 6th PERIOD	Early Dismissal, of course!

Vacation Journal

How can you remember every awesome thing you do this vacation? Write it down! Write down what you do each day—good stuff and bad stuff (hopefully, there won't be much of that). You can start below!

DATE: _____

DEAR VACATION DIARY,

TODAY, I _____

_____

_____

_____

_____

_____

_____

_____

_____

_____

_____

WOULD YOU RATHER . . . ?

Are you and your friends bored sitting around the house with nothing to do? Well, what would you rather be doing? Here are some fun ideas that will help you figure it out.

Would you rather have **FOUR-DAY WEEKENDS ALL YEAR LONG** or **SIX MONTHS OF NO WEEKENDS AND THEN SIX MONTHS OF VACATION?**

Would you rather **HAVE THE ABILITY TO FLY** or **BE ABLE TO TALK TO ANIMALS?**

Would you rather **SPEND YOUR VACATION IN TAHITI** or **ON MARS?**

Would you rather **EAT A BANANA AND TUNA FISH OMELET** or a **PICKLES AND CHOCOLATE PIZZA?**

Would you rather **SPEND A WEEK AT YOUR DESK IN SCHOOL** or **BURIED IN A GIANT PUDDLE OF MUD?**

SCRAMBLED SUMMER

These vacation words have gotten all jumbled up. Can you unscramble them?

1. XLRAE

_____

2. TYPRA

_____

3. EPESL

_____

4. HBAEC

_____

5. MSUMRE

_____

WHAT'S YOUR VACATION PERSONALITY?

Not all vacations are created equal! Everyone has different ideas about how they want to spend their free time. What's *your* vacation personality? Take this quiz to find out! Match up your answers with the numbers on p. 16. Then add up those numbers for the 411 on your vacation personality.

1. ON THE FIRST DAY OF YOUR VACATION, YOU LIKE TO

a. sleep until noon . . . or maybe until dinner.
b. get up at dawn so you can pack as much into the day as possible.
c. watch cartoons all morning in your pajamas, then go out with your friends.

2. IF YOU COULD SPEND ONE DAY DOING ANYTHING YOU WANTED, YOU WOULD

a. go bungee-jumping off a cliff in South America.
b. lie on a beach in Hawaii.
c. rent out an amusement park just for you and your friends.

3. AT SLEEPOVERS, YOU'RE ALWAYS

a. asleep as soon as the lights go out.
b. wide-awake all night long.
c. whispering with friends until you can't stay up any longer.

4. IF YOU WON A MILLION DOLLARS, YOU WOULD

a. buy a tropical island and move there.
b. throw the biggest party the world has ever seen.
c. go on a month-long shopping spree and buy everything you've ever wanted.

5. YOU WISH YOU COULD SPEND THE SUMMER

a. at camp with your friends.
b. napping in the sun.
c. traveling around the world.

Answers:
1. a = 1, b = 3, c = 2
2. a = 3, b = 1, c = 2
3. a = 1, b = 3, c = 2
4. a = 1, b = 2, c = 3
5. a = 2, b = 1, c = 3

13-15 X-TREME VACATIONER

GO! GO! GO! GO! YOU'RE FULL OF ENERGY AND YOU'RE READY TO HAVE AN EXCITING, AMAZING, UNBELIEVABLE TIME EVERY SINGLE SECOND OF THIS VACATION. YOU'RE NOT GOING TO WASTE A MINUTE—THERE'S JUST TOO MUCH TO DO! JUST DON'T FORGET: TAKE A DEEP BREATH AND RELAX ONCE IN A WHILE—YOU MIGHT EVEN ENJOY IT!

9-12 Life of the PARTY

AS FAR AS YOU'RE CONCERNED, FRIENDS = FUN, AND YOU DON'T CARE WHAT YOU'RE DOING AS LONG AS YOUR BFFS ARE ALONG FOR THE RIDE. **JUST DON'T FORGET:** MAKE SURE YOU FIND SOME TIME ON THIS VACATION TO DO WHAT **YOU** WANT TO DO.

5-8 LAZY BONES

Okay, so you're lazy, lazy, lazy. So you like sleeping late, lying around, and relaxing. So what? You're on vacation, right? JUST DON'T FORGET: Get some exercise occasionally—your couch may be comfy, but there's a whole world out there to explore!

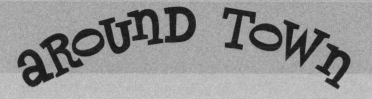

AROUND TOWN

YOU CAN'T SPEND A WHOLE VACATION LOCKED
UP IN YOUR HOUSE WATCHING TV, BUT DON'T WORRY,
YOU DON'T NEED TO TRAVEL VERY FAR TO HAVE FUN!
LOOK OUT THE WINDOW: WHEREVER YOU LIVE—CITY,
COUNTRY, SUBURBS—THERE'S A WHOLE WORLD OF FUN
WAITING JUST OUTSIDE YOUR DOORSTEP.

HOW MUCH DO YOU REALLY KNOW ABOUT
YOUR HOMETOWN? WELL, NOW YOU'VE GOT
AN ENTIRE VACATION TO FIND OUT....

WHAT ARE YOU WAITING FOR?

MaP IT!

Use this space to draw a map of your town, including all the exciting places you might want to go this vacation. (You can ask your parents to help you out with this one—or go to your local library and ask for help finding a map of your town.)

Here are some suggestions for places you might want to include on your map:

*Your house * Your friends' houses * Where your parents work * Zoo * Pool * Library * School [Unless you're pretending it doesn't exist. Ha!]*

DAYTRIP DELIGHT

You don't have to hop on a plane or cross an ocean to have an adventure. Here are some ideas for places where you might find some fun in your hometown:

Zoo

Does your town have a local zoo or a petting zoo? Then why not spend a day talking to the animals? Maybe you can pet a llama, spot a leopard, or even ride an elephant!

Museum

Just because you're on vacation doesn't mean you can't learn something. And museums make learning fun! Check out a science museum to learn about how the universe works, or a natural history museum to hang with the dinosaurs.

WELCOME

World's LARGEST EAR OF CORN!

ENTER

GIFT SHOP

Pool

Do you have a local pool where you can cool off and laze away your days relaxing in the sun or zooming down a giant water slide? Hey, just don't forget the sunscreen!

Amusement Park

Towering roller coasters! Super-sonic spinning rides! Carnival games! Cotton candy! 'Nuff said.

FUN IN THE SUN SUGGESTION: Some of these places may have just-for-kids programs, so ask your parents to call to find out. Maybe you can get a special behind-the-scenes tour of your favorite hometown hotspot!

Daytrips I took this vacation:

_____

_____

_____

_____

_____

_____

_____

_____

_____

HOMETOWN HIJINKS

Even if you decide not to take these daytrips, you can still joke about them—after all, laughter is the best medicine for boredom!

ZOO

What time is it when an elephant sits on your fence?

Time to get a new fence!

MUSEUM

What do you call a dinosaur that breaks everything it touches?

A "Tyrannosaurus Wrecks"

SNAP!

POOL Why should you always swim the backstroke after you eat?

Because you shouldn't swim on a full stomach.

LIBRARY

What's black and white and red all over?

A book with a sunburn.

Ode to a Swimming Pool

Oh, swimming pool
So cold and blue,
Are you aware
That I love you?

Your diving board,
Your lovely slide,
Which is best?
I can't decide!

On sunny days
That never end—
Oh, swimming pool,
You're my best friend!

TOWN TRIVIA

How much do you know about your hometown? Here's your chance to test your stuff. Some of the answers are facts, and the rest are a matter of opinion. Either way, you will be an expert by the time you're done!

1. STATE WHERE YOU LIVE:

2. YOUR STATE CAPITAL:

3. YOUR STATE BIRD:

4. NAME OF YOUR TOWN:

5. OLDEST BUILDING IN TOWN:

6. NEWEST BUILDING:

7. BEST SECRET SHORTCUT:

8. MOST AWESOME HOUSE IN YOUR TOWN:

9. BEST RESTAURANT:

10. WORST RESTAURANT:

11. BEST HOUSE/NEIGHBORHOOD FOR
TRICK-OR-TREATING ON HALLOWEEN:

12. BEST PLACE TO GO SHOPPING:

13. BEST SWIMMING SPOT:

14. BEST PLACE TO SPEND
a DAY OFF:

15. UGLIEST BUILDING:

THE SUMMER TIMES

Your Town, Your State

Today, 2003

Late Edition
Today: Sunny
Tomorrow: Still Sunny
Day After Tomorrow: Yup, still sunny

Boy and girl find treasure! Dog helps.

Nose for News

Want to learn more about where you live? Then why don't you get together with a few friends and start a town newspaper? You can report on what your friends are doing, or what's going on in your house, or you can interview people around your town and sniff out some local news! (Just remember: Don't talk to anyone you don't know without your parents' permission!) Making your own newspaper is easy —here's how you can get started:

HIRE A STAFF

Okay, first you'll need a couple of reporters. Though you could create a newspaper all on your own, it might be more fun with several friends (plus, that way you get to be the boss)! First, get a few of your friends together and then decide who wants to write about what. Finally, send them out to collect their stories.

NOSE FOR NEWS

So what's new? Everything! You can turn anything into a news story if you try. Did your sister lose her favorite shirt? Did your friend just move into a new house? Is your local toy store happening 24/7—you just never noticed before!

INTERVIEWING

Once you've found your story, you need to get some people is just about asking them the right questions— what they saw, what they did, what they think. Just make sure you get their name spelled right—the rest of the questions are up to you!

WRITE IT UP

Now that you've got the facts, it's time to put them together. The best news stories cover all the bases, and that means they answer the five "W"s: who, what, when, where, and why. Got all that?

having a sale? Once you start looking around, you'll realize that things are

information. And how can you do that? By asking, of course! Interviewing

Of course, it's great if your story can be fun and interesting, too, but don't forget that the key word here is "news," so make sure you get in all the facts!

ROOM FOR FUN

A newspaper doesn't have to be all news. There are lots of other ways that you can fill up space: comic strips, weather reports, gossip horoscopes, columns—anything you want. After all, it's your paper, so your

decision is final!

GET IT TOGETHER

Your last step is putting all of your stories together into a newspaper. You can copy them all down onto a few sheets of paper (check out a real newspaper for ideas)—or you can just staple all of the articles together, like a magazine. Make a bunch of copies and hand them out to anyone who might want one— or you could even try to sell them!

LOST AND FOUND

This unlucky kid is lost on his way to the amusement park—can you help him find his way?

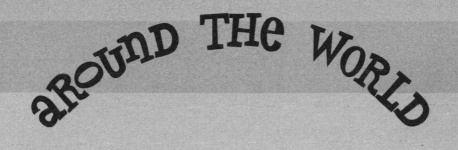

AROUND THE WORLD

ONE OF THE BEST THINGS ABOUT BEING ON VACATION
IS THAT YOU HAVE TIME TO SEE AND DO SO MANY
NEW THINGS. AND THERE'S PLENTY TO DO—REMEMBER,
THERE'S A WHOLE WORLD OUT THERE FOR
YOU TO EXPLORE!

SO, WHERE WILL YOU GO ON THIS VACATION?
TO THE CITY? TO THE BEACH? TO THE MOON?
WHETHER YOU TAKE A CAR TRIP, A PLANE TRIP,
OR JUST A TRIP THROUGH YOUR IMAGINATION, TRAVELING
CAN BE AN INCREDIBLE WAY TO MEET NEW PEOPLE,
SEE NEW PLACES, TRY NEW THINGS,
AND HAVE TONS OF FUN.

SO, TURN THE PAGE . . .

THE WORLD IS WAITING!

GEOGRAPHY GAME

Each of these clues is about a different place—can you figure out the right answers and fill in the crossword?

ACROSS:

4. Where you'll find Hollywood, San Francisco, and lots of beaches

9. Smallest state in the U.S.

10. Home of the Taj Majal

DOWN:

1. Has more people than any country in the world

2. Has had two queens named Elizabeth

3. Country north of the United States

5. The "Big Apple"

6. Home of the Eiffel Tower

7. Country south of the United States

8. Say "aloha" to this land of hula skirts and luaus

31

you and the u.s.a.

Take a look at the map below—how many of these states have you been to? Color in or mark each state you've visited—then make a list of the ones you still want to see!

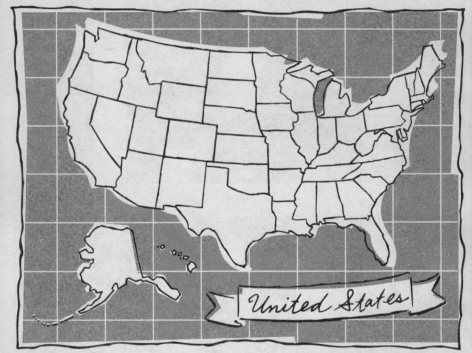

United States

States I want to visit:

_____	_____
_____	_____
_____	_____
_____	_____
_____	_____

Far and Wide

I'M GOING ON A TRIP TODAY,

TO SOMEWHERE STRANGE

AND FAR AWAY.

ROUND AND ROUND THE WORLD I'LL GO,

AND WHERE I'LL STOP,

I JUST DON'T KNOW.

I DON'T CARE WHERE OR WHAT I SEE,

AS LONG AS IT'S

ALL NEW TO ME.

WHAT'S NEW?

What's the best thing about traveling? Everything is new—new people, new places, new foods, new languages, new everything! So, what new things have you discovered this vacation?

New places I saw:

New people I met:

New foods I tried:

New languages I learned:

New things I liked:

New things I disliked:

----

aRe We THeRe yeT?

There's just one problem with going places—you have to get there first. And that can mean spending a long, long time trapped in a car or on a plane. But however you get where you're going, there's no need to be bored. Here are a couple of great ways to pass the time!

Geography on the Go

Don't worry—this game doesn't involve homework! It's lots of fun. Here's how you play: Someone starts by saying the name of a place. Town, city, state, country, continent—it doesn't matter, as long as it's real! Whatever the last letter of the place name is, the next person has to come up with a place that *starts* with that letter. And then the next player needs a place name that starts with the last letter of *that* place. For example:

Player #1: Kansa**s**
Player #2: **S**outh Dakot**a**
Player #3: **A**frica

And on and on and on. If you can't think of a place name and have to pass, you're out—so the last person left in the game wins!

Storyteller

You can't watch TV when you're stuck in the car, but with this game, you can make your *own* entertainment. All you need for this game are a couple friends (or parents, or twerpy brothers and sisters) and some imagination. The first person should start to tell a story, but should stop after the first sentence. After that, the next person should take over, and fill in the next sentence. Then just keep going back and forth until your story is done!

Stumped? Here are some ideas for story openers:

IT WAS THE BEST OF TIMES, IT WAS THE WORST OF TIMES....

Janice wasn't surprised when it started to rain—but she WAS surprised when it started raining frogs....

HOWARD HID UNDER THE TABLE AND HELD HIS BREATH, TRYING TO BE AS QUIET AS HE COULD....

It was a dark and stormy night....

Twenty Questions

This guessing game is as simple as can be: Player #1 thinks of an object and player #2 tries to guess what it is. How? Player #2 gets to ask twenty "yes" or "no" questions—and *only* twenty questions. Here's an example:

QUESTION #1: Is it bigger than a toaster?

ANSWER: *Yes*

QUESTION #2: Is it bigger than an elephant?

A: *No*

QUESTION #3: Is it something that you would have around the house?

A: *Yes*

QUESTION #4: Is it something you would keep in the kitchen?

A: No

QUESTION #5: In the bedroom?

A: Yes

QUESTION #6: Is it electronic?

A: No

QUESTION #7: Is it a piece of furniture?

A: Yes

QUESTION #8: Is it soft?

A: Yes

Can *you* guess what
the object is?

Of course, if you're going to take a long trip, you're definitely going to need some tunes. Here are some perfect songs for your road trip mix:

"Drive My Car" by The Beatles

"You Drive Me Crazy" by Britney Spears

"Open Road Song" by Eve 6

"Ticket to Ride" by The Beatles

"Summertime" by Will Smith

"In My Car" by The Beach Boys

"Traveling Man" by Dolly Parton

FM 103.5
ROAD TRIP RADIO

ON

LOUD
LOUDER
LOUDEST

IMAGINATION VACATION

Stuck at home? No problem—check out these great books and movies about traveling to exciting new places, and you can see the world without ever leaving home!

MOVIES

What a Girl Wants
Around the World in 80 Days
The Voyages of Dr. Dolittle
The Lizzie McGuire Movie

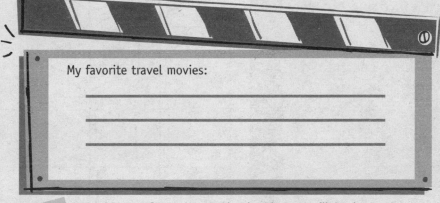

My favorite travel movies:

_____

_____

_____

BOOKS

United Tates of America, by Paula Danziger

The Cay, by Theodore Taylor

Stowaway, by Karen Hesse

Oh, the Places You'll Go, by Dr. Seuss

Pippi Longstocking, by Astrid Lindgren

Magic Tree House: Hour of the Olympics, by Mary Pope Osborne

My favorite travel books:

_____

_____

_____

MUSTANG MIX-UP

Have you always wanted your own car? Well, now you can have this cool convertible . . . if only you can figure out how to put it back together. Copy the lines from each numbered box into the empty box with the same number—and before you know it, you'll have a car of your very own!

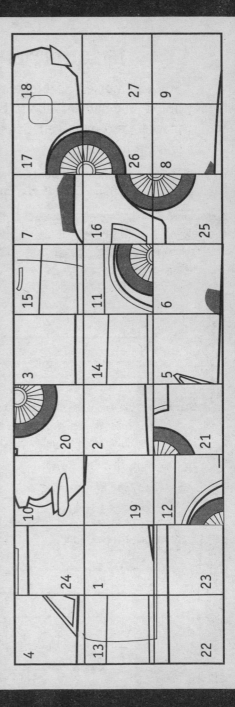

1	2	3	4	5	6	7	8	9
10	11	12	13	14	15	16	17	18
19	20	21	22	23	24	25	26	27

WISH YOU WERE HERE

One of the best things about going away is that you get to send postcards to all the people that you've left behind. Use the space below to draw a postcard of a place you've been (or a place you want to go)and then write about all the great adventures you had there!

PSST... Did you know that the post office will send almost anything through the mail, as long as it has a stamp and an address on it? Instead of sending a normal postcard to your friends, why not send out a cereal box postcard? Take an empty box of cereal—one with a fun picture on it—and cut out postcard-size pieces in any shape you like. Then write your message on the back, stick on a stamp, and send it off to your friend. Think it'll arrive? You'll have to wait and see!

FUNNY FILL-INS!

Here's a story about a wild vacation adventure for you and your friends to fill in. Just get your friend to come up with one of each kind of word listed below, then fill in the story on the next page. Who knows what you'll come up with!

NAME OF PERSON: _____

PLACE NAME: _____

ADJECTIVE: _____

VERB (PAST TENSE): _____

NOUN: _____

ADJECTIVE: _____

NOUN (PLURAL): _____

ADJECTIVE: _____

NOUN (PLURAL): _____

VERB (PAST TENSE): _____

NOUN: _____

EXCLAMATION: _____

ADJECTIVE: _____

VERB: _____

LAST SUMMER, MY FRIEND _____ AND I WENT
(NAME)

TO _____. IT WAS A _____ TRIP.
(PLACE NAME)   (ADJECTIVE)

WE _____ THERE ON A _____. I MET LOTS
(VERB, PAST TENSE)   (NOUN)

OF _____ _____, WHO TOLD ME ABOUT ALL THE
(ADJECTIVE) (PLURAL NOUN)

_____ _____ TO SEE. ON THE LAST DAY, I _____
(ADJECTIVE) (PLURAL NOUN)   (VERB, PAST TENSE)

THE BIGGEST _____ I HAVE EVER SEEN.
(NOUN)

" _____ !" I SAID. "THAT IS _____ !"
(EXCLAMATION)   (ADJECTIVE)

THIS IS ONE VACATION THAT I

AM NEVER GOING TO _____.
(VERB)

TRAVEL JOURNAL

What kind of round-the-world adventures have you had this vacation? Make a list of the exciting places you've been and the things you've seen, so that you'll never forget!

_____

_____

_____

_____

_____

_____

_____

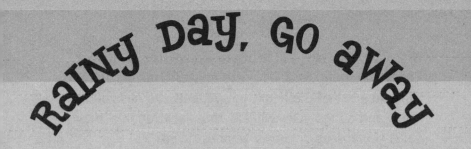

RAINY DAY, GO AWAY

THERE'S NOTHING WORSE THAN BEING
STUCK INSIDE ALL DAY WITH NOTHING TO DO.
*(Well, you could be stuck inside all day
with homework to do. . . .)*
BUT SOMETIMES, THE WEATHER DOESN'T
REALIZE THAT YOU'RE ON VACATION.

HAVE NO FEAR, BOREDOM-BUSTING FUN IS HERE!
THESE IDEAS AND ACTIVITIES WILL HELP YOU
HAVE AN ADVENTURE-FILLED DAY—EVEN IF YOU
HAVE TO HAVE ALL YOUR ADVENTURES
IN YOUR OWN LIVING ROOM.

THUMBS-UP?

What do you like to do when you're stuck inside? Read? Watch movies? Listen to music? Use this space to make a list of the books you've read, movies you've seen, and songs you've heard this vacation. Do they get a thumbs-up . . . or a thumbs-down?

BOOKS I'VE READ: RATING (*circle one*):

_____ THUMBS-UP / THUMBS-DOWN

_____ THUMBS-UP / THUMBS-DOWN

_____ THUMBS-UP / THUMBS-DOWN

_____ THUMBS-UP / THUMBS-DOWN

_____ THUMBS-UP / THUMBS-DOWN

MoViES i've SEEN:

RATING (*circle one*):

_____ THUMBS-UP / THUMBS-DOWN

_____ THUMBS-UP / THUMBS-DOWN

_____ THUMBS-UP / THUMBS-DOWN

_____ THUMBS-UP / THUMBS-DOWN

_____ THUMBS-UP / THUMBS-DOWN

SoNgS i've HEARD:

RATING (*circle one*):

_____ THUMBS-UP / THUMBS-DOWN

_____ THUMBS-UP / THUMBS-DOWN

_____ THUMBS-UP / THUMBS-DOWN

_____ THUMBS-UP / THUMBS-DOWN

_____ THUMBS-UP / THUMBS-DOWN

The Land of Counterpane

By Robert Louis Stevenson

When I was sick and lay a-bed,
I had two pillows at my head,
And all my toys beside me lay,
To keep me happy all the day.

And sometimes for an hour or so
I watched my leaden soldiers go,
With different uniforms and drills,
Among the bed-clothes, through the hills;

And sometimes sent my ships in fleets
All up and down among the sheets;
Or brought my trees and houses out,
And planted cities all about.

I was the giant great and still
That sits upon the pillow-hill,
And sees before him, dale and plain,
The pleasant land of counterpane.

"The Land of Counterpane" is one of the most
famous poems ever written about being
BORED, BORED, BORED
and stuck inside all day. Next time you're bored,
why not try writing your own poem?

✹ ✹ ✹

....

....

....

....

....

....

....

....

....

....

FILL IT IN

You don't have to be Shakespeare to write poetry . . . but it sure does help! This Shakespeare poem has lost some of its words—can you come up with new ones? There's only one rule: Each of the lines is marked with a letter— and all the lines with the same letter have to rhyme.

(A) Shall I compare thee to a summer's _____?

(B) Thou art more lovely and more _____.

(A) Rough winds do shake the darling buds of _____,

(B) And summer's lease hath all too short a _____.

(C) Sometime too hot the eye of heaven _____,

(D) And often is his gold complexion _____;

(C) And every fair from fair sometime _____,

(D) By chance or nature's changing course _____;

(E) But thy eternal summer shall not _____,

(F) Nor lose possession of that fair thou _____;

(E) Nor shall Death brag thou wander'st in his _____,

(F) When in eternal lines to time thou _____:

(G) So long as men can breathe or eyes can _____,

(G) So long lives this, and this gives life to _____.

SHAKE IT UP

Here's another fun way you can use someone else's words to help you write your own poem. Take a page from a magazine or a newspaper, and cut out 5–10 words. You can either cut out words at random, or you can pick the ones you like. Then put all the pieces of paper in a plastic bag and shake it up.

Pick them out one by one and write them down on the page in that order—there's your poem! Now lay all the words down on the table faceup and pick out the words you want to use in the order you want to use them. Write them down in that order. Now you've got two poems that use the same words . . . and say completely different things!

POEM #1

POEM #2

CAMPOUT

Sure, it's raining outside, but inside your house, the weather's just fine. So why not go camping?

If you have a tent, pitch it in your
living room—and if you don't have a tent, you
can always make one out of sheets and blankets.
(Just get your parents' permission first!)
Then you can invite your friends for a
sleepover and spend the night "camping in"!

LOST AND LAZY

These lazy words are lost in the word find and are too lazy to find their way out. Can you help out by finding and circling them all? The words are hidden across, down, and even diagonally!

NAP   COUCH   RAIN   BED   TIRED
SLEEP   WARM   LAZY   BORED

```
S  K  I  H  N  A  P  Q  S  B
R  A  I  N  G  W  V  S  B  O
F  C  T  W  A  R  M  S  B  F
C  O  S  I  K  R  A  D  O  N
M  U  Y  L  R  D  B  F  R  Y
Y  C  Y  L  N  E  S  E  E  R
W  H  L  R  Z  J  D  D  D  F
A  A  A  S  S  L  H  Z  U  U
Z  X  Z  Y  W  M  G  G  J  K
H  F  Y  B  A  S  L  E  E  P
```

CRAZY COMICS

Don't you wish that *you* could draw your *own* comic adventures? Well, now you can—just follow these basic tips, and you'll be drawing your own comics in no time!

It's easy to draw a face. First, draw a circle.

Then fill in facial features, like the eyes, nose, mouth, eyebrows, cars, and hair.

Making facial features different shapes changes the expression of a face from happy to angry to surprised, so play around with the features. Check out some of the faces that we drew below.

Drawing bodies seems hard, but it isn't as long as you break everything down into simple geometric shapes.

1. For the top part of the body, draw a rectangle. Draw a small half-circle at the top—that's where the neck will be.

2. Draw a triangle on each side of the rectangle. These will be the sleeves of the T-shirt.

3. Now draw the neck and arms.

4. Draw two long rectangles below the top part of the body. These will be the pant legs. Now add two semicircles at the bottom of the rectangles—these are the shoes.

5. Now add a face to complete your character. Add details like pockets to the pants and a design to the T-shirt.

 USE THESE CLOUDLIKE BALLOONS TO SHOW WHAT A CHARACTER IS THINKING.

USE THESE OVAL-SHAPED BALLOONS TO SHOW WHAT A CHARACTER IS SAYING.

Below, there are a bunch of empty panels for you to start your adventures or funnies! Not enough room? Use some scrap paper to draw bigger comic strips.

And remember: Every good comic strip has a *beginning*, *middle*, and *end*.

SECRET CODE CHALLENGE

Can you decipher this rainy-day message? The key to the code is at the bottom of the page—but it's up to you to figure it out.

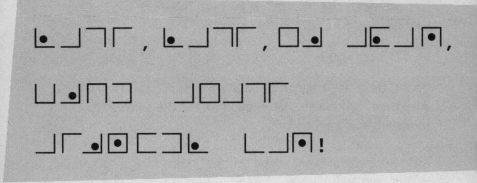

A	C	D		O	Q	R
E	G	H		S	T	W
I	M	N		X	Y	Z

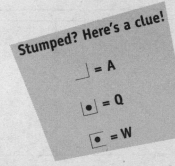

Stumped? Here's a clue!

⌐ = A

|•| = Q

|•⌐ = W

easy as aBC

Here's another super-secret code for you and your friends to share, so that no one can ever read your secret messages. This code assigns a number to each letter—you can make up your own code by assigning new numbers. As long as your friends have the key, they'll always be able to decipher your messages. But first, try using this code to figure out the secret message below:

KEY:

A = 1	H = 8	O = 15	V = 22
B = 2	I = 9	P = 16	W = 23
C = 3	J = 10	Q = 17	X = 24
D = 4	K = 11	R = 18	Y = 25
E = 5	L = 12	S = 19	Z = 26
F = 6	M = 13	T = 20	
G = 7	N = 14	U = 21	

__ - __ - __ - __   __ - __   __ - __ - __   __ - __ - __ - __
20 8   9   19   9   19   20 8   5   2   5   19 20

__ - __ - __ - __ - __ - __ - __   __ - __ - __ - __ - __!
22 1   3   1   20 9   15 14   5   22 5   18!

NOW YOU SEE IT, NOW YOU DON'T

What's the best way to keep your secrets a secret? Write them in invisible ink! Here's how you can make your own:

YOU NEED:
>   2 TSP OF WATER
>   1 TSP OF BAKING SODA
>   CUP
>   SPOON
>   PAINTBRUSH

1. PUT 2 TEASPOONS OF WATER IN A CUP AND ADD 1 TEASPOON OF BAKING SODA.

2. STIR UNTIL THE BAKING SODA DISSOLVES.

3. DIP YOUR PAINTBRUSH INTO THE "INK," AND WRITE YOUR MESSAGE.

4. TO MAKE THE MESSAGE APPEAR, HOLD THE PAPER NEAR A LIGHTBULB UNTIL THE WRITING TURNS BROWN. (BE CAREFUL NOT TO TOUCH THE PAPER TO THE LIGHTBULB—AND DON'T TOUCH THE LIGHTBULB YOURSELF. IT'S HOT!)

USE THIS SPACE TO WRITE SOME
MESSAGES IN YOUR NEW INVISIBLE INK—OR
MAKE UP YOUR OWN METHOD FOR SWAPPING
SECRET MESSAGES WITH YOUR FRIENDS!

_____

_____

_____

_____

_____

_____

_____

_____

_____

_____

_____

_____

PEN PALS

You may spend a lot of time
e-mailing and instant-messaging
your BFFs, but do you ever write them
letters? Sure, snail-mail is a lot slower...
but it can also be a lot more fun. Maybe you
have friends who are away at camp, or maybe
you're the one who's far from home. Or maybe
you and your best friend live next door to
each other—just because you see each
other ten times a day, doesn't mean you can't
write each other some letters!

Who do you want to write to? Use the next
page to get started on a letter to your BFF.
Tell your friend what you've been up to—
and how much you miss her!

Dear .... ,

....

....

....

....

....

....

....

....

....

....

....

....

.... ,

....

CARING CARE PACKAGE

As long as you're sending a letter, why not send a care package along with it? A care package is a great way to show someone that you care—and it can also be a lot of fun to put together! Here are some ideas for what you can include:

BROWNIES

HOMEMADE CARD

PHOTO OF YOU AND YOUR FRIENDS

MIX TAPE OR CD

MAGAZINE

COMIC STRIP OF YOUR ADVENTURES TOGETHER

YOUR FAVORITE POEM

A FUNNY COMIC STRIP YOU'VE DRAWN

And why not come up with a few ideas of your own? The best care packages are the most personal ones, so pick out some things you know your friend will love!

FUN IN THE SUN

THE RAIN HAS COME AND GONE,
THE SUN IS SHINING, IT'S A BEAUTIFUL DAY,
AND YOU KNOW WHAT THAT MEANS:

IT'S TIME TO GO OUTSIDE!

GET OUT OF THE HOUSE AND INTO
THE BACKYARD,
OR THE PLAYGROUND,
OR THE POOL—
IT DOESN'T MATTER WHERE YOU GO,
AS LONG AS YOU HAVE FUN!

YOU'RE IT!

Want to play outdoors, but sick and tired of playing the same old games all the time? Why not try something new with an old favorite? You already know how to play tag, right? One person is chosen to be "It," and he or she has to catch everyone else. If you get caught, you're out. But is that all? No way! There are a ton of different kinds of tag—it could take you a lifetime to play them all. Here are just a few:

TV TAG

When the person playing "It" tags someone, they must freeze in place. To unfreeze them, another player must tag them and yell out the name of a TV show. Each TV show can only be said once.

FLASHLIGHT TAG

This is a combination of tag and hide-and-seek, and has to be played at night. The person playing "It" should close his or her eyes and count to twenty while everyone else runs and hides. Then the person playing "It" has to go looking for them—with a flashlight. The other players can switch their hiding places whenever they want, but if they get "tagged" with the flashlight beam, they're out.

STICKY TAG

Start by picking two people to be "It." They should hold hands and chase the other players. Whenever someone gets caught, he or she gets "stuck" to "It," and now all three have to hold hands and chase. When a fourth person is caught, "It" can split up into two and two players, or choose to stay together. (As more and more people stick to "It," you can split up as many times as you want, as long as it's always in pairs of two or more players.) Keep playing until everyone gets caught.

REVERSE TAG

Choose one person to be "It." Then everyone who is not "It" should count to five while "It" runs away—after five seconds, everyone else should start chasing and try to tag the person who is "It." If you tag him or her, then you become "It" and have to run away.

JUMP FOR JOY

If you love to jump rope, then you know that the most fun part is the rhyme you sing while you're jumping. Here are a few for you to try:

MISS MARY MACK

Miss Mary Mack Mack Mack
All dressed in black black black
With silver buttons buttons buttons
All down her back back back.

She asked her mother mother mother
For fifteen cents cents cents
To see the elephant elephant elephant
Jump over the fence fence fence.

He jumped so high high high
He touched the sky sky sky
And he never came back back back
Til the fourth of July July July!

MISS LUCY

Miss Lucy had a baby

And she named him Tiny Tim.

She put him in the bathtub

To see if he could swim.

He drank up all the water.

He ate up all the soap.

He tried to eat the bathtub

But it wouldn't go down his throat.

Miss Lucy called the doctor,

Miss Lucy called the nurse.

Miss Lucy called the lady with the alligator purse.

TEDDY BEAR

Teddy Bear Teddy Bear turn around.

Teddy Bear Teddy Bear touch the ground.

Teddy Bear Teddy Bear show your shoe.

Teddy Bear Teddy Bear that will do.

Teddy Bear Teddy Bear go upstairs.

Teddy Bear Teddy Bear say your prayers.

Teddy Bear Teddy Bear turn off the light.

Teddy Bear Teddy Bear say good night.

SUNNY DAYS

It's another beautiful day. Can't think of anything to do? Well, you've got all the time in the world to play out in the sun, so have some fun. Check out these top ten ways to enjoy a sunny day! (Just don't forget your sunscreen.)

10. GO ON A BIKE RIDE

9. HAVE A PICNIC

8. GO SWIMMING

7. GO IN-LINE SKATING

6. TAKE A NATURE WALK

5. GO TO A BASEBALL GAME

4. EAT AN ICE-CREAM CONE

3. TAKE A NAP IN THE GRASS

2. PLAY TAG—EVEN IF YOU THINK YOU'RE TOO OLD FOR IT

AND YOUR NUMBER ONE, ABSOLUTE FAVORITE WAY TO HAVE FUN ON A SUNNY DAY IS . . .

1. _____

CLOUD COVER

Oh, no! The sun is trapped behind all the clouds—can you help the sunlight find its way out, before this vacation day is ruined for everyone?

JUST IMAGINE

When you stare up at the clouds, what do you see? Just a bunch of funny white shapes? Or do you see cars and horses and castles—or anything else your imagination comes up with? Take a look at these clouds below—what do you see in them? Grab a pencil or some markers and turn these clouds into anything you'd like. The sky's the limit!

LAUGH RIOT

Playing outside isn't just fun, it's funny! Check out these silly summer jokes:

WHAT DID THE BEACH SAY WHEN THE TIDE CAME IN?
Long time, no sea.

WHEN IS AN UMPIRE LIKE A TELEPHONE?
When he makes a call.

WHAT KIND OF HAIR DO OCEANS HAVE?
Wavy.

WHERE DO RACE CARS GO SWIMMING?
In a car pool.

PUZZLE PLAY

Can you solve the clues and fill in the right outdoor words in the crossword below?

ACROSS:
****

4. good to drink or to sell

5. something you find on the beach

7. the worst thing for a picnic

8. how you feel when there's too much sun

9. "Don't forget to come inside when

    it gets _____."

DOWN:
****

1. can use for climbing or for shade

2. where to find swings and monkey bars

3. "Would you like to play a _____?"

5. source of light

6. midday meal

STaR LIGHT, STaR BRIGHT

Sure, it's fun to play in the sun, but what happens when the sun goes down and the stars come out? There's no reason for your fun to end! The night sky is filled with amazing things to see—you just have to know how to look.

Astronomers have divided the night sky into
88 <u>constellations</u>—groups of stars connected by imaginary lines.
Here are some of the most famous ones—how many can you find?

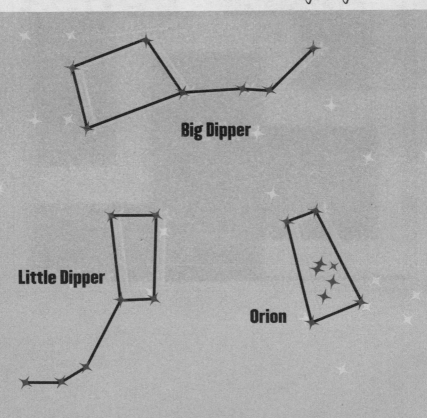

Big Dipper

Little Dipper

Orion

Cassiopeia

Ursa Major

Ursa Minor

STARRY SUGGESTION

You probably don't have a telescope lying around the house, but that doesn't mean you can't be an amateur astronomer. If you have a pair of binoculars, try looking at the night sky through them. The stars are so far away that it won't make much difference—but what happens when you aim them at the moon?

RIDDLE ME THIS

Now are you ready to really test your brain? Try these brainteasers on for size. Don't flip out if you can't figure them out. Just flip the book to read the answers!

What can you catch, but not throw?

A COLD.

How much dirt is in a hole 3 feet wide and 5 feet deep?

THERE IS NO DIRT IN A HOLE.

If two's company and three's a crowd, what are four and five?

NINE.

You're in a dark room, with a candle, a wood stove, a gas lamp, and only one match. What do you light first?

THE MATCH.

Some months have thirty days, some months have thirty-one. How many have twenty-eight?

ALL OF THEM.

ALL'S WELL THAT ENDS WELL

IT'S ALMOST HERE—THE DAY YOU'VE BEEN
DREADING FOR YOUR VACATION:
THE LAST DAY.
YOU'VE HAD AN AMAZING TIME, BUT NOTHING LASTS
FOREVER . . . AND SOONER OR LATER, YOU'LL
HAVE TO GO BACK TO SCHOOL.

BUT NOT YET!
YOU'VE STILL GOT A LITTLE MORE TIME LEFT,
SO WHY NOT MAKE THE MOST OF IT?
MAKE THIS THE BEST VACATION
YOU'VE EVER HAD!

PARTY TIME!

How better to celebrate the end of your vacation than to have a party? Or better yet, lots of parties! Here are some helpful hints for things to keep in mind as you put your party together:

THEME

The first thing you need to do is figure out what kind of party you want to have. What do you think of these themes?

Back-to-School Party

Hawaiian Beach Party

Sleepover Party

60s Party

Pool Party

Make-Your-Own-Ice-Cream-Sundaes Party

Roller Skating Party

INVITATIONS

Once you've got a theme, you'll know what kind of invitations you need. Why not make your own? That way, you can make them as wild and wacky, as awesome and outrageous as you want them to be. But first, you need to figure out who you're going to invite.

INVITATION LIST FOR MY PARTY:

....

....

....

....

....

....

....

....

....

....

FOOD

Next, you're going to need some snacks for your party. What will you serve? Anything you want—it's *your* party!

We've even included an easy-to-make pizza recipe below!

Food to serve at my party:

_____

_____

_____

FRENCH BREAD PIZZA
(*serves 2*)

Ingredients:

French bread

Tomato sauce

Grated cheese

Chopped veggies

1. Make sure to ask for an adult's help.
2. Preheat the oven to 425°F.
3. Slice bread lengthwise.
4. Place both halves of bread on aluminum foil-covered baking pan.
5. Cover each with sauce, toppings, then cheese.
6. Bake for 15 minutes. Let it cool for a minute.
7. Now CHOW DOWN!

Rate It!

Sure, your vacation was good—but *how* good? Here's a fill-in that'll help you figure it out!

This vacation has been:

awesome   Good

          okay   terrible

The best three things I did this vacation were:

_____

_____

_____

The one thing I wish I had done is:

_____

If I could change one thing about this vacation, it would be:

_____

FINDERS, KEEPERS

You may be headed back to school, but don't forget, another break is coming up soon. Take a big step toward your next vacation by finding the hidden vacation words in the puzzle below. (Words are hidden across, down, and diagonally.)

BREAK SUMMER TRiP VACATiON CAMP FUN SPORTS GAMES SWIMMiNG BEACH

```
F S S W I M M I N G
B R W Q A S E G G S
C R E O S W T F F U
R U E O X P H U Q M
V A C A T I O N X M
J A M P K G M R M E
L Z H M V C A U T R
B E A C H A W M O S
Y B Y T H M E N E V
E V T R I P C S S S
```

BACK TO SCHOOL

YOU WOULDN'T BELIEVE
WHAT A SUMMER I'VE HAD!
BUT NOW THAT IT'S DONE,
I REFUSE TO BE SAD.

. . .

I'LL MISS THE BASEBALL
AND FISHING AND FUN—
AND I HAVE TO ADMIT
THAT I'LL MISS ALL THE SUN.

. . .

BUT THERE'S ONE BIG THING
TO BE HAPPY ABOUT . . .

ONLY 180 MORE DAYS,
UNTIL SCHOOL IS OUT!

PHOTO FINISH

Use the next few pages to paste down photos of you and your friends having vacation fun—or draw some pictures of all the exciting things you guys did together. That way, you'll never forget what an awesome vacation you had — after all, vacations may end, but memories last forever!

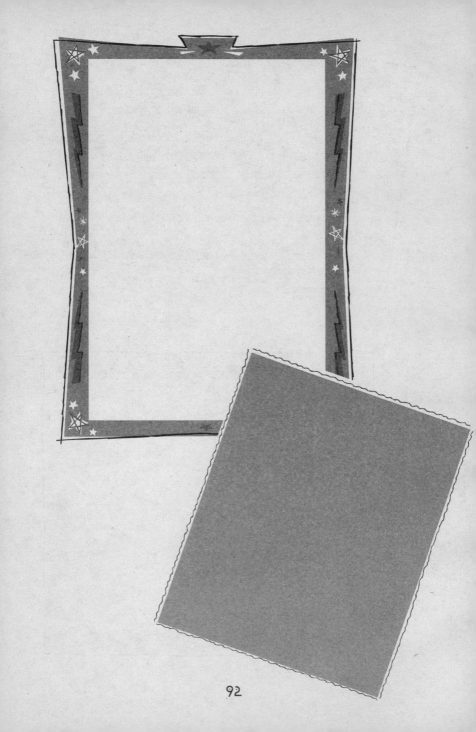

COUNTDOWN CALENDAR

Don't forget, there's one good thing about starting school again: It means that another vacation is on its way! Can't wait? Why not count down the days so that you know exactly how much time you've got left. Get a calendar—or make your own—and mark the day that your next vacation starts. Then each night, you can cross off another day, and know that you're one day closer to **FUN**!

ONLY _____ DAYS LEFT
UNTIL MY NEXT VACATION!!!

answers:

p. 13
1. RELAX
2. PARTY
3. SLEEP
4. BEACH
5. SUMMER

p. 28

p. 31

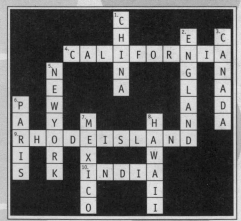

p. 39
The object is a BED.

p. 42

1	2	3	4	5	6	7	8	9
10	11	12	13	14	15	16	17	18
19	20	21	22	23	24	25	26	27

p. 58

p. 62

RAIN, RAIN, GO AWAY, COME AGAIN ANOTHER DAY!

p. 63

THIS IS THE BEST VACATION EVER!

p. 75
There are two ways to
get through this maze.

p. 79

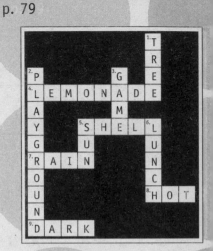

p. 88